This book is designed to be read initially by children and adults together. It is a book about the impact the diagnosis of a mother's cancer can have on a young child's life. It is a starting point for discussion, giving the adult a way in to ask about the child's own experience of a difficult situation. On each page ... ... colour in.

Second Edition

Text © Eileen Wheeler 2006
Illustrations © Iiris Maanoja 2006

Granted under licence to CLAN

ISBN 978-0-9551642-6-2

Published by:

CLAN Cancer Support
CLAN House
120 Westburn Road
Aberdeen
AB25 2QA

Printed by XIC

MUM HAS CANCER

By Eileen Wheeler

&

Illustrated by Iiris Maanoja

CLAN
cancer support for all

A little while ago my mum
was very tired and didn't
want to go to the park or
play with me in the garden.

Dad went with mum to
see the doctor. She sent
her to the hospital for
lots of tests.

These weren't like the tests I do at school. The doctors took
some blood from her, and she went into big machines which
took pictures of her insides. They are called scans and x-rays.

The hospital doctors told mum that her body isn't working properly. She has a disease called cancer, and needs medicine to make her better. The doctors don't know why it happens. No-one is to blame for mum having cancer, and you cannot catch cancer or pass it on to anyone else.

Cancer happens when the tiny cells that make up our body don't behave themselves. The cells work at super-fast speed and grow out of control. Eventually that bit of the body stops working the way it should.

First mum went into hospital to have an operation. The surgeon cut out the bit that was damaged.

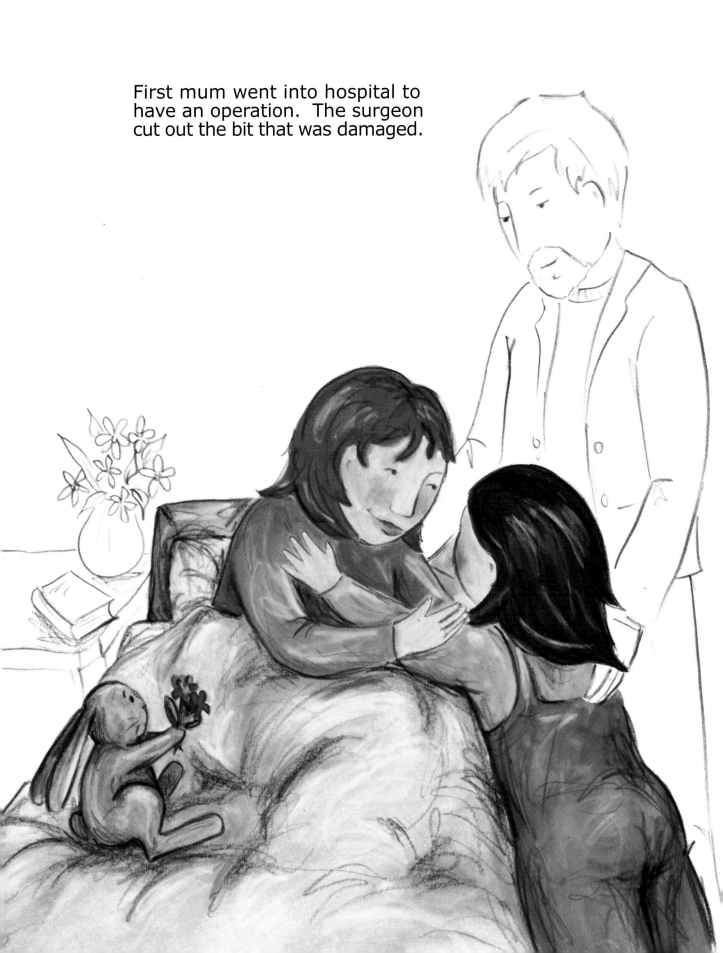

When she came home she was sore and stiff. I like to snuggle up to her in her bed in the morning, but I had to be very careful not to touch her sore bit.

Sometimes mum seemed upset and cried. At first I was worried, but mum said she was just happy to be home again. Some of mum's friends cried when they visited. Mum says it is okay to cry as tears let the feelings out and that is good.

After a few weeks mum had to stay in hospital again to get some medicine called chemotherapy. On those days dad does not have to go to work until after I start school, and he finishes early so he can collect me. I like to know who will collect me from school.

The medicine goes into mum through a tube into her arm. Sometimes it makes her very sick – like when I ate too much chocolate, sweets, crisps, cake and ice cream at Megan's birthday party.

The medicine made mum's hair fall out. When this happened I thought she looked very strange and I didn't like seeing her without her scarf. But then I got used to it. It is just my mum without her hair. She still gives me hugs, cooks my food, takes me to school and sometimes tells me off, just like she did when she had all her hair. And it will grow back when she stops having the chemotherapy medicine.

When we are in the supermarket or the park some people stare at mum. It is rude to stare and I get angry with them. But mum just takes a deep breath, smiles at them, says hello, then gives me a hug and I feel better.

Mum doesn't like being ill and wants
to get better. She will have to get
the medicine for a long time. So
we will have to be patient, and give
the medicine time to do its work.
But then things will go back to how
they were before she had cancer.